ADVENTURES OF THE
SUPERKIDS

BY PLEASANT T. ROWLAND

ILLUSTRATED BY
MERYL HENDERSON
LORETTA LUSTIG
DOUG ROY

CONTRIBUTING WRITERS
SHIRLEYANN COSTIGAN
ANNE MARTIN
VALERIE TRIPP

ROWLAND READING FOUNDATION
MIDDLETON, WISCONSIN

ISBN 978-1-59833-387-9   AD33387   1 2 3 4 5 6 7 8 9 10 WC 16 15 14 13 12 11 10 09

Table of Contents

Unit 1

<u>sh</u>	<u>ch</u>	<u>tch</u>
shelf	bench	latch
shop	branch	patch
shovel	lunch	scratch
crash		stitch
radish		
radishes		

I   my   she   her   he   his

O.K.   super

5

A Patch in a Pinch

Rip! Sal split his pants.
"I must fix my pants," said Sal.

Cass ran onto the bus.
"My cat is stuck on a branch,"
said Cass. "Will you help?"

Sal sat on the bench.
"No," said Sal. "I can not."

Cass was upset. She ran to Hot Rod.
"I must get my cat," she said.
"But Sal will not help."

Hot Rod ran to Sal. He said, "Will you help Cass get her cat?"

"No," said Sal. "I can not."

"Will you get up and help?" Hot Rod said.

"No," said Sal. "I can not."

Hot Rod got mad.
"O.K., I will help Cass."

Hot Rod left in a huff.

10

Sal got up to patch his pants.
But Alf ran onto the bus.
As quick as a wink, Sal sat back
on the bench.

Alf said, "The lid on my lunch box
is stuck. Will you help fix it?"

"No," said Sal. "I can not help you.

I can not help Cass.

I can not help Hot Rod.

I can not stand up."

"Can I help you?" Alf said.

Sal said, "Yes. I split my pants."

"No problem," said Alf. "I will patch the pants for you."

"Super," said Sal. He began to grin.

Alf left to patch Sal's pants.

"I will fix Alf's lunch box," said Sal.

Sal twisted the latch on the lunch box. Twist, twist, pop! "Super!" said Sal. "I did it!"

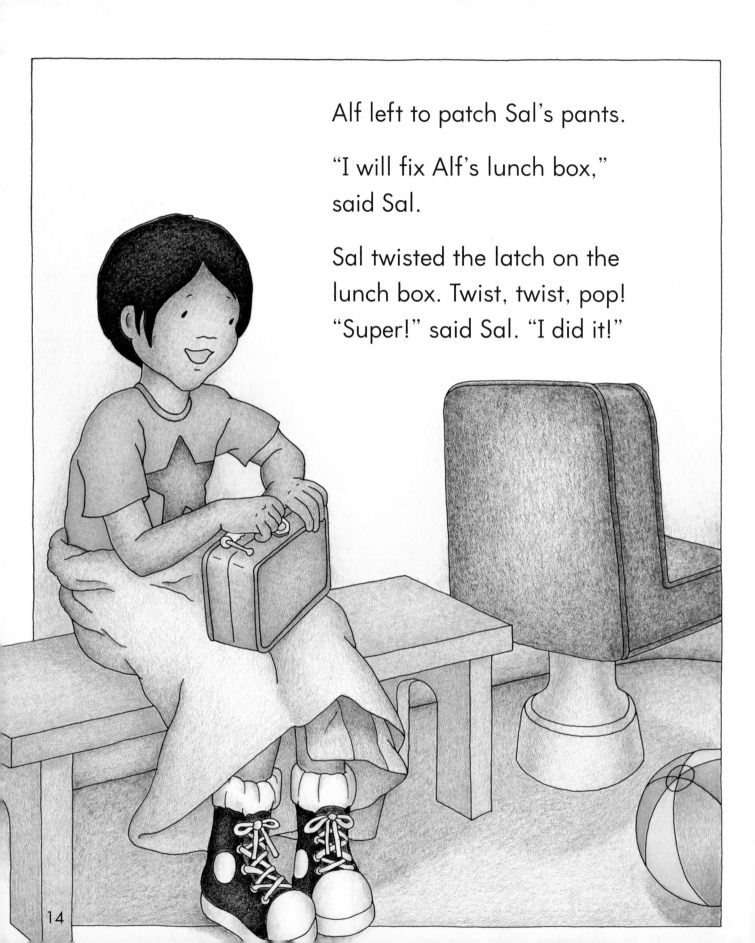

At last Alf got back. Sal put on his pants. He handed the lunch box to Alf.

"Super!" said Alf.

Sal patted the patch on his pants. "Yes, just super!" he said. "Let's help Cass and Hot Rod get the cat."

Ettabetta's Radish Patch

I got a pack of radishes.
It did not cost a lot.
I got my shovel
And began to dig a plot.

I planted the radishes.
The plants got lots of sun.
Pop up! A radish patch!
It was lots of fun.

The Patch-it-up Shop

"My Patch-it-up Shop is super," said Doc.

But just as Doc said it, her  fell. Clank!
As Doc ran to pick it up, a step fell in.
Crash!

Doc ran to get her fix-it kit on the shelf.
The shelf tilted. Her kit slid off. Bump!

Doc had to sit on the bench to fix
the shelf. A leg on the bench snaps.
Crack!

"Well, I must fix my Patch-it-up Shop,"
said Doc.

Doc got tacks to patch up the step.

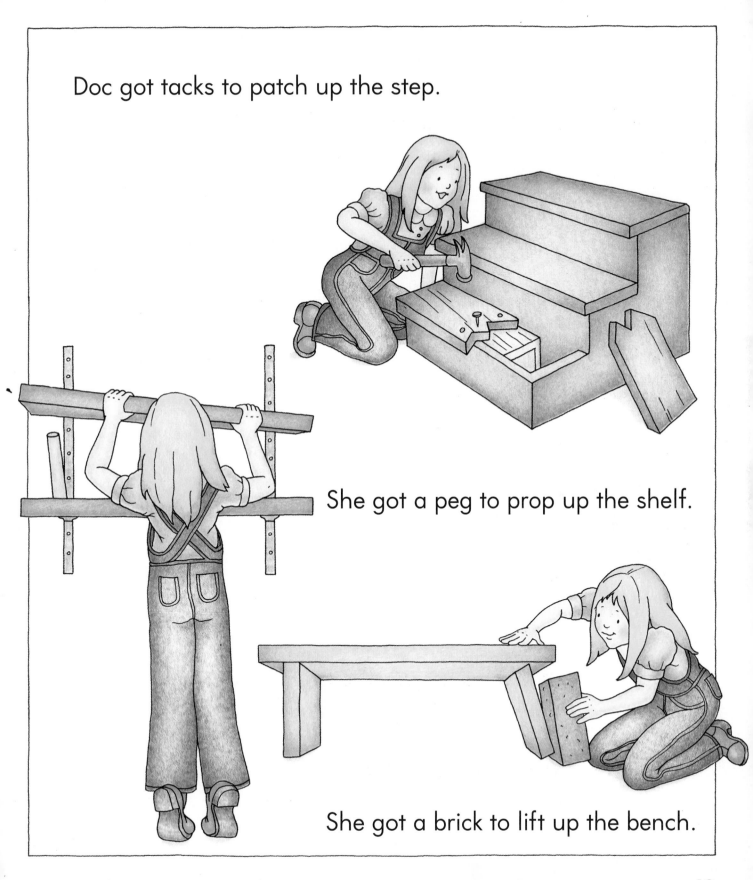

She got a peg to prop up the shelf.

She got a brick to lift up the bench.

Doc put up her  and said, "At last my Patch-it-up Shop is super!"

PATCH, STITCH, AND MEND
You bust it, I fix it.
DOC'S PATCH-IT-UP SHOP

You scratch it up,
Doc will patch it up.

You rip it up,
Doc will fix it up.

I fix
trucks
dolls
bats

You crack it up,
Doc will tack it up.

Unit 2

What Can You Get with a Nickel?
What a Pet!

th

thank

thanks

that

them

think

this

cloth

with

where   what   why   when   which   who

O.K.   super

What Can You Get with a Nickel?

Frits sat on the steps of Ben's shop with his chin in his hands.

"I think Frits is upset," Ben said to his parrot.

"Who? Who?" said the parrot.

Ben said, "Frits, what is the problem?"

"What? What?" said the parrot.

"Shush!" said Ben.

"Doc is sick," said Frits. "I wish I had a gift for her. But what can I get with just a nickel?"

"Well," said Ben, "you can not get much."

"Not much! Not much!" said the parrot.

"Shush!" said Ben.

Ben and Frits sat and sat. At last Ben said, "I can not think of a gift. But let's check the back of my shop."

"Where?" said the parrot.

"The back of my shop," said Ben.

"O.K.," said Frits.

"This is the back of my shop," said Ben. "This is where I cut and stitch. This is where I fix belts. What a mess!"

"Mess! Mess!" said the parrot.

"Shush!" said Ben.

Frits spotted a bag on the top shelf.

"That bag has scraps of cloth in it," said Ben.

"Will you sell the cloth for a nickel?" said Frits.

"Yes, I will," said Ben. He handed it to Frits.

"Yes, yes!" said the parrot.

Frits put his nickel on the bench. "Thank you," he said and left the shop in a rush.

When Frits got back, he handed a box to Ben.

"What is this?" said Ben.

"What? What?" said the parrot.

27

"Moccasins for Doc," said Frits.

"Doc will like them," said Ben.
"You did a super job."

"Thanks," said Frits.

"What?" said the parrot.

"I said thanks!" said Frits.
And he ran off to visit Doc.

28

What a Pet!

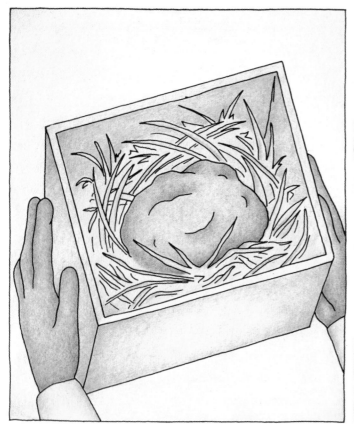

A rock is not a pet.

Yes, it is. Just flip it on its back.

What did I tell you? Flint is a pet! Flint is a big, fat frog!

Unit 3

ng	le
thing	bubble
wings	fiddlestick
long	little
strong	simple
	Twinkle
	wiggle

do   have   show   how   me   a

story   blow

Fiddlesticks

"Let's tell a fiddlestick story," said Oswald. "It is simple. I begin a story. I tell a little bit of it. When I stop, I pass the fiddlestick to the next kid."

"That kid adds a little bit to the story. Then that kid passes the fiddlestick to the next kid. When the fiddlestick gets back to me, I end the story."

This is The Bubble Gum Story.

Jessica Twinkle had a big pack of bubble gum.

She began to blow a big bubble. Puff, puff, puff.

Jessica's bubble did not pop. It got big.

Stop! I pass the fiddlestick to Tic.

34

Just then the wind began to blow. It lifted the bubble up and Jessica went up with it.

"How can I get off? I am stuck!" said Jessica.

Stop! I pass the fiddlestick to Frits.

The bubble drifted up, up, up.

"How did I get in this mess?" said Jessica.

"What?" said a thing on the top of the bubble.

"That is odd. What is on top of my bubble?" said Jessica.

Stop! I pass the fiddlestick to Alf.

"I am a pelican," said the thing on the top of the bubble.

"I am Jessica," said Jessica, "and I am stuck. Will you help me?"

"Yes, I will help you," said the pelican.

Stop! I pass the fiddlestick to Toc.

"I can pop the bubble with my bill. That will get you off," said the pelican.

The pelican bit the bubble. The bubble went POP!

Jessica began to drop. "Help me!" said Jessica. "Help, help, help!"

Stop! I pass the fiddlestick to Lily.

38

Quick as a wink, the pelican was next to Jessica.

She got on his strong back. It was not long until the pelican landed.

Jessica got off. "Thank you," she said.

"It was fun," said the pelican. He lifted his wings and left.

Stop! I pass the fiddlestick to Oswald.

Just then, Jessica's pal ran up.

"I got a pack of gum," he said. "Do you like to blow bubbles?"

"You bet I do," said Jessica with a grin. "I blow super bubbles!"

"Is that the end of the story?"
said Lily.

"Yes, that is the end," said Oswald.

"Fiddlesticks!" said Lily.

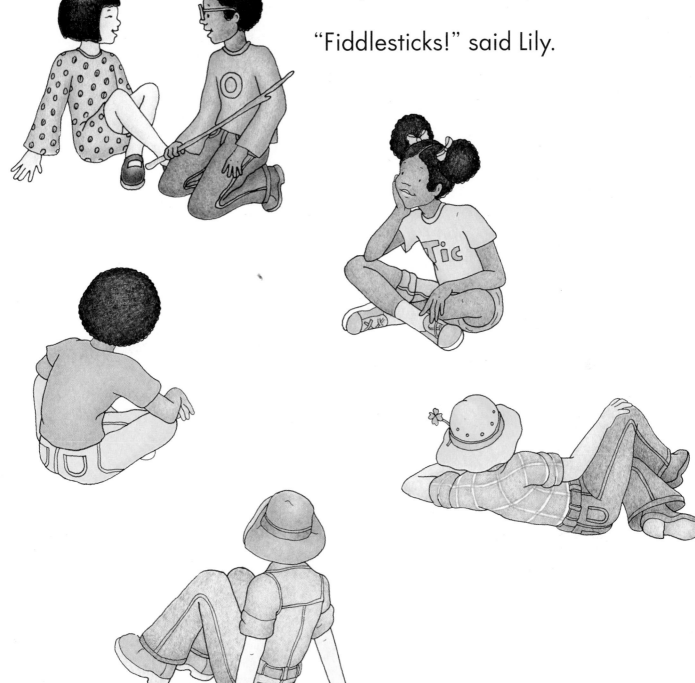

Super Scrub-a-matic

Golly is a mess and must have a bath,
  have a bath,
    have a bath.

Golly is a mess and must have a bath.
  Super scrub-a-matic!

I will show you how I scrub him,
  how I scrub him,
    how I scrub him.

I will show you how I scrub him.
  Super scrub-a-matic!

Next he gets a big, big splash,
a big, big splash,
a big, big splash.

Next he gets a big, big splash.
Super scrub-a-matic!

Then the dog must do the wiggle,
do the wiggle,
do the wiggle.

Then the dog must do the wiggle.
Super scrub-a-matic!

43

Golly licks and kisses me,
kisses me,
kisses me.

Golly licks and kisses me.
Super scrub-a-matic!

At last I like to show him off,
show him off,
show him off.

At last I like to show him off.
Super scrub-a-matic!

Unit 4

In a Pickle 46
Golly Went Sniffing 54

<u>er</u>	<u>ed (ed)</u>	<u>ed (d)</u>	<u>ed (t)</u>
after	lifted	filled	asked
longer	twisted	giggled	clenched
other		puzzled	cracked
pepper		smelled	crushed
		yelled	scratched
			sniffed
			unclenched
			yanked

look   your   the   was   are   for

In a Pickle

Cass was mad. Her hand was stuck
in a plastic pickle bottle. She looked
at the bottle.

"How did I get in this mess?" she said.

Just then Cass went past Lily.
She looked at Lily.

"Willikers!" Lily said. "What is
that on your hand?"

Cass said, "It is a pickle bottle.
I am stuck."

Lily giggled. "Well, Cass, it looks as if
you are in a pickle," she said.

"My ring fell in the bottle," said Cass.
"I put my hand in the bottle to get
the ring. Then my hand got stuck."

"Your ring? What ring?" asked Lily.

"My bubble gum ring," said Cass.

"What is a bubble gum ring?" asked Lily.

"It is a ring I sent for after I got a pack of bubble gum," said Cass.

"Where is your ring?" asked Lily.

"In my hand," said Cass.

"Which hand?" asked Lily.

"This hand!" said Cass, and she lifted up the bottle.

LOOK! LOOK! LOOK!
Get your Flubble Bubble flip-top ring!
The top of the ring flips up!
It is as much fun as the gum was!
Flubble Bubble flip-top rings are super!
Send for your ring fast!

"I think I can get the bottle off," said Lily.

Cass held on to the bench.
Lily held on to the bottle.
She yanked and yanked.
But Cass was stuck.

Cass kept her hand clenched.
She held on to her ring.
Lily yanked and twisted the bottle,
but Cass was still stuck.

"Ug! You are still in a pickle!"
said Lily.

Lily scratched her chin and
looked puzzled.

"How did you get your big fist
in the little bottle?" she said.

Cass lifted her other hand.
"Like this," she said. "Look."

Lily looked at Cass's hand.
Then she looked at the
fist in the bottle.

"Unclench your fist," she said.
"Let the ring drop."

Cass unclenched her fist.
The ring fell to the bottom of
the bottle. Pop! The bottle fell off.

"Lily!" yelled Cass. "That did it!"

Just then Oswald ran up to them.

"What is happening?" he asked.

"Nothing, Oswald. But thanks to Lily,
I got my ring back, and I am
no longer in a pickle!" said Cass.

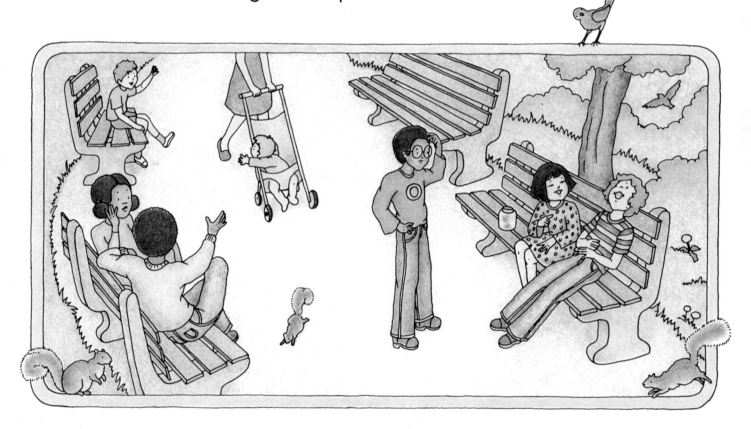

Golly Went Sniffing

Golly went sniffing
in a big trash can.
He smelled a pickle
and a crushed tin pan.

He sniffed an eggshell
and a cracked glass dish,
a bit of salad,
and a scrap of fish.

Golly sniffed a bottle
in the big trash can.
It was filled with pepper,
and off Golly ran!

ing	ed	ing	ed
bumping	asked	beginning	flapped
fussing	crashed	flapping	flipped
thumping	huffed	flipping	flopped
	melted	getting	grabbed
	whispered	sopping	hopped
			stopped

helping	covered	running	grinned
	jumped	shopping	hugged
	kissed	sitting	yapped
	licked		zigzagged
	sniffed		
	yelled		

there   from   be   to   we   or

The Monster Under the Bus

BUMP!

"What is that?" asked Tac.

"I bet it is a monster," said Tic.
"It is under the bus!"

"There are no monsters," said Toc.

"There is a TV show with a monster
in it," said Tic. "The TV monster is
The Blob."

"In the beginning The Blob is little. Then it gets bigger and bigger and begins flipping and flapping. Then it gobbles up little kids!"

Just then the thing under the bus FLIPPED, FLAPPED, and CRASHED!

"Gosh! I bet that <u>is</u> a monster under the bus," said Tac.

"Monsters are just pretend," said Toc.

Just then the thing under the bus HOPPED, FLOPPED, and HUFFED!

"It is <u>not</u> pretend," said Tic.
"The Blob <u>is</u> under the bus."

The thing under the bus began THUMPING and BUMPING!

"How can we stop The Blob?" asked Tac.

"If The Blob gets wet, it will melt," said Tic. "We can get it wet with the sprinkler."

"<u>You</u> can get it wet," said Tac. "<u>I</u> am not getting off this bus."

"Will you kids stop fussing?" said Toc. "The thing under the bus is <u>not</u> The Blob. I will get the sprinkler, just to show you."

Toc ran off the bus and grabbed
the sprinkler.

She put the sprinkler under the bus.

And just at that second, the thing
under the bus stopped!

It did not thump. And it did not bump.

"What did I tell you?" whispered Tic. "The monster melted when it got wet. It must be The Blob."

"Well, the thing <u>did</u> stop when the sprinkler hit it," said Toc. "Let's look under the bus and check."

Tic, Tac, and Toc looked under the bus and began to giggle.

There sat the monster. There sat a sopping
wet dog and a sopping wet cat.

"You big wet blobs!" said Tic, Tac, and Toc.

Yuck! Yuck!

Frits was sitting with Oswald on the grass when Doc ran up.

Doc yelled, "Little Dominic went shopping with his big sister, and he got lost! Did he run past you?"

"Yes," said Frits. "Dominic is sitting on the bus."

Doc, Frits, and Oswald ran to the bus. Little Dominic was not on the bus.

"I bet he got off when I was not looking," said Frits.

"Look," said Oswald. "He left his socks and sandals on the bus."

Then Frits said, "I bet Golly can show us where Dominic is. Golly likes to smell things. Golly can track Dominic if he smells his socks."

Frits grabbed a sock and jumped off the bus. "Golly, Golly," Frits said. "Smell this sock and look for little Dominic. Show us where Dominic is."

Golly sniffed and sniffed the sock.
Then he began running up the block.

"Golly is running fast," said Doc.
"Let's catch up with him."

The dog zigzagged up the block.
He sniffed as he went.

At last Golly stopped.
He yapped and yapped!

There was Dominic, sitting in
a mud puddle. He was covered
with mud from top to bottom.

Golly yapped and licked Dominic
on the chin.

"Dog!" said Dominic, as he
hugged Golly's neck.

"Yuck," said Frits. "Little Dominic
is a mess."

"Let's get him back to his big sister,"
said Oswald.

"O.K. But you pick him up," said Doc.

"Yuck. Not me," said Oswald.

"Yuck. Not me," said Frits. "You pick
him up, Doc. You got us into this mess.
This is your problem."

But just then Dominic's sister ran up
the block.

"Dominic!" she yelled. "There you are."
She ran up and grabbed little Dominic.
She hugged him and kissed him.
Dominic's sister was covered with mud!

Then Dominic's sister grabbed Frits
and Oswald and hugged them!

"Thank you for helping me look
for Dominic," she said. "Thank you."

Frits was covered with mud.
Oswald was covered with mud.
But Doc was not covered with mud.
She just grinned at them and said,
"Yuck! Yuck!"

Unit 6

The Foolish 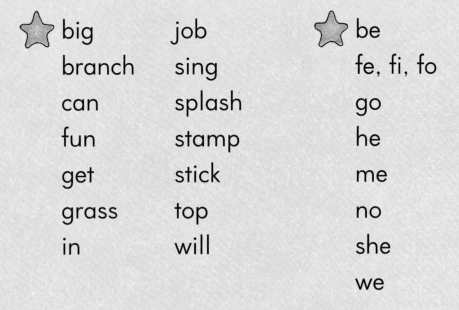 72
When I Am a 82

⭐ big	job	⭐ be
branch	sing	fe, fi, fo
can	splash	go
fun	stamp	he
get	stick	me
grass	top	no
in	will	she
		we

said   only   you   out   of   here

foolish

⭐ When a word has only one vowel and ends in one or more consonants, the vowel is short.

⭐ When a word has only one vowel and it is at the end, the vowel is long.

The Foolish

"Let's pretend," said Ettabetta. "Sal, you be the foolish 🧑. Alf, you be the 🐘. I will be the 🐒."

"A foolish 🧑? Ug," said Sal. "I will be a clever 🧑. I do not like acting foolish."

"We are only pretending," said Ettabetta.

"Well, O.K.," said Sal.

The kids began pretending.

The  yelled, "Fi! Fo! Fum! Fe!
The  has to go with me."

The  put the  in the .
Then he unhitched the ladder.
It fell onto the grass.

"Why did you do that?" asked the .
"How can I get out of here?"

"Fe! Fi! Fum! Fo!" said the .
"I will never let you go."
Then he left.

The  yelled to the ,
"Help! I am stuck!"

"Only I can get you out of here!"
said the .

The  tossed the ladder up.
But the  missed it.
The ladder fell on top of the .

"I can not get the ladder up to you,"
said the .

"I am trapped!" yelled the .

The  yelled, "Fe! Fi! Fum! Fo!
Run fast, ! Go! Go! Go!"

"I will attack the !" said the .

Ettabetta said, "Stop pretending,
Alf and Sal. I am trapped
up here."

"No, you are not," said Sal. "I can get you. But that is a job for the . I am only a foolish !"

"Then let's pretend that this  is clever," said Ettabetta.

"O.K.," said Sal. "If I can be a clever , I will help you."

The clever  got a long stick. He passed it up to the . Then he put the ladder on the end of the stick.

"Lift the stick up," he said to the .

Up went the ladder. The  hung it on the branch. Quick as a wink, she was standing next to the .

"Thanks, ," said the . "I am glad that you are not foolish."

Sal grinned. "Fi! Fum! Fo! Fe! A clever —that is me!"

When I Am a 🦭

When I am a 🦭,
I will swim and splash and run.
Lots of kids will visit me
And have a lot of fun!

How will it be? How will it be,
When we can pretend?
How will it be? Have fun with me.
What will we pretend?

When I am a ,
I will ring a big, big bell.
Then how the  will tremble
When I tramp and stamp and yell!

How will it be? How will it be,
When we can pretend?
How will it be? Have fun with me.
What will we pretend?

83

When I am a ,
I will have a dragon pet.
And he will sing me dragon songs
Until the sun has set.

How will it be? How will it be,
When we can pretend?
How will it be? Have fun with me.
What will we pretend?

84

Unit 7

Kites 86
Today I Got a Gift 97

⭐ came   make
cute   name
drive   note
drove   plane
five   smile
gave   time
hope   use
kites   wave
like   while
line   white

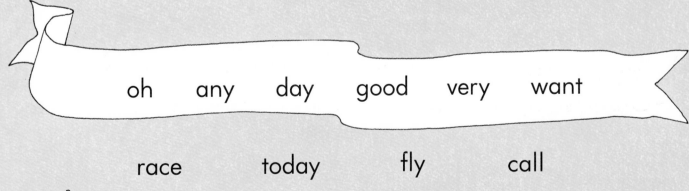

oh   any   day   good   very   want

race   today   fly   call

⭐ When a word ends in an e and has one other vowel, the e is silent and the other vowel is long.

Kites

It was the day of the big race. Hot Rod planned to drive the Fast Cat. But his helmet was missing.

"I can not be in the race if I do not have a helmet," Hot Rod said. "It must have dropped off the back of the Fast Cat."

"Did you have your name in it?" asked Tac.

"No," said Hot Rod. He bit his lip. "I think my helmet is lost."

"We want to help you get your helmet back," said Tac.

"Yes," said Lily. "We can put notes in lots of shops."

"We can put an ad in the Sun Press," said Cass.

"Oh, what good will that do?" said Hot Rod. "There is not any time. The race begins in a little while."

Just then Tac spotted a plane with a banner hanging from the back.

Tac snapped her fingers. "I have a good plan," she said. "We will fly a note! Quick, Superkids! Run and get your kites."

The kids came back with five kites.
Tac printed big letters on them.

"Stand in a line and fly the
kites," Tac said to the kids.

A big gust of wind came up.
Up went the kites. Hot Rod
looked at the note
on them.

"Do you think the kites will help us get the helmet back?" asked Hot Rod.

"Oh, I hope so," said Tac. "The note has Gus and Gert's number to call."

It was close to race time. Hot Rod was very upset.

"Oh, it is not any use," Hot Rod said. "I think I am out of luck."

Just then Gert came running up. She said, "I do not understand this. I just got a call from a man. He has the helmet you want. He will be here any second."

The kids jumped and yelled, "We did it! We did it!"

Just then Gert spotted the kites. "Oh," she said. "You put a note on the kites. You kids are very clever."

A man drove up in a truck.
He gave a wave with his hand.

"Is this your helmet?" he asked.

"Oh, yes!" said Hot Rod. "Thank you
very much. I can still make it to the
race."

"Run, Hot Rod! Run!" yelled the kids.

Hot Rod ran and hopped into the Fast Cat.

95

Hot Rod got to the track just in time. He looked up and spotted the kites. He began to smile.

"My pals are fantastic," said Hot Rod. "Let's go, Fast Cat. Let's win this race for the Superkids!"

Today I Got a Gift

Today I got a gift I like
and it is just for me.
I got a little speckled fish
as cute as it can be.
Up it swims, up to the top.
I think it spotted me!

Today I got a gift I like
and it is just for me.
I got a kite, just like a fish,
but made of silk and string.
Up, up it swims into the wind.
A wiggling, swimming thing!

finished   dived

fishing   hiked

helping   liked

jumped   making

stretched   raked

stuffed   raking

yelled   saving

dropped   sliding

setting   waving

slipping

tugged

tugging

boy   two   about   girl   over   before

 To read a word with an ending, take off the ending. If there is only one consonant before the ending, the vowel is usually long.

Golly Helps

The Superkids hiked to the lake.

"Let's set up camp before dinner," said Lily.

Golly wanted to help.

Hot Rod was raking. Golly jumped
into the piles of twigs and sticks.

"I just raked those!" said Hot Rod.
"Get out, Golly!"

Lily was setting up the tent.
Golly ran over to help.
He got tangled up in the ropes.

"Golly!" said Lily. "You are not
helping. Go!"

Golly went to help Cass make dinner.

"Golly, you are making a mess!" said Cass.
"Get lost!"

Frits was fishing. Golly wanted to help.
But he tipped over the basket of fish.

"Golly, you are a pest!" said Frits.
"Get out of here!"

Golly gave up. The Superkids did not
want his help. He ran off and sat next
to the lake. He felt sad.

Then Golly spotted a little boy waving his hands.

"Help! I dropped my truck!" yelled the boy.

Golly dived into the lake. SPLASH! He got the truck and paddled back to the boy.

"Thank you for saving my truck!"
said the boy.

The boy gave Golly two bites of his
hot dog. Before long, the snack
was finished.

"So long, Dog," said the boy.

Golly spotted a bunch of kids
in a rope-tugging contest. He ran over
and bit the end of the rope. He tugged
and tugged. Golly liked helping the kids.

The boys and girls on the other side began slipping and sliding. After two big tugs, those kids tumbled over the line.

"We won!" yelled the kids on Golly's side. "Thank you for helping us, Dog!"

"We will make you a big dinner,"
said a girl.

Golly stuffed himself.

When dinner was over, the boys and
girls said, "You can help us any time!"

Golly went back to the Superkids.

"Golly, where did you go?" said Cass.
"Here is your dinner."

But Golly just stuck up his nose.

Alf said, "Golly, you must help finish this dinner."

But Golly just stretched out and napped in front of the tent. He had finished his helping for that day.

Unit 9
The Straw Horse 114
The Contest 122

☆ beads   needles   cheaper
bean   paid   Dearing
blue   real   seemed
boat   sail
chair   see
each   wheels
ears
green

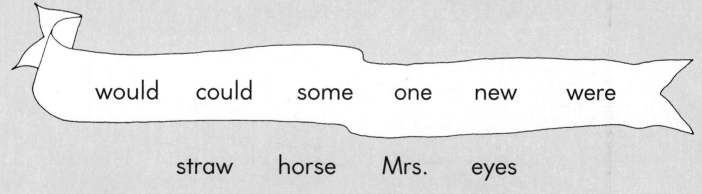

would   could   some   one   new   were

straw   horse   Mrs.   eyes

☆ When a word has two vowels together, the first is usually long and the second is silent.

The Straw Horse

Lily and Ettabetta liked to visit
Mrs. Dearing's shop. There was
a big closet in the back of the
shop. It was full of used things
that the girls could have fun with
any time.

One day the girls spotted some new things in the closet. There was a duck with a missing wheel, a doll's chair with three missing legs, and a boat with a ripped sail.

"Look!" said Ettabetta. She held up a little straw horse.

The horse had straw ears and a straw mane. It had a brave smile. But it had no eyes. Lily and Ettabetta liked the straw horse very much.

"The horse looks so sad," said Lily. "Let's make new eyes for it."

"O.K.," said Ettabetta. "What could we use for eyes?"

"Buttons!" said Lily. "Let's look for some."

A box in the closet had wheels, ribbon, and a little bean bag in it. There were needles, pins, and bits of string in the box. But there were no buttons.

"Mrs. Dearing sells new beads in her shop," said Lily. "Let's see if she has some that we could use for eyes."

Lily spotted some big white beads with blue dots in the middle. Each bead cost one dime.

"These green beads are cheaper than the white ones," said Ettabetta.

"Yes," said Lily. "But the green beads would not be as good for eyes."

"I have one dime," said Ettabetta.

"So do I," said Lily. "Let's get two white beads."

The girls paid for the beads. Lily stitched the
beads on the horse and gave it two new eyes.

The straw horse seemed to smile.

"I think it likes its new eyes," said Lily.

Mrs. Dearing said, "Thank you very much, girls! I will give you your dimes back. You made the horse as good as new. I can sell it in my shop."

"The new eyes make the little horse look real," said Ettabetta.

And the little horse seemed to smile a bigger smile.

The Contest

The sun and the wind had a contest on a fine spring day. This is what happened.

Sun, I am stronger than you. Just look! Puff! Puff! Puff!

No, Wind, I am much stronger than you.

 Just then a man in a cape came past.

 Wind, let's have a contest to see who is stronger. If you can make that man take off his cape, you win.

 That is simple. Just look at this. Puff! Puff! Puff!

 That wind is so strong! I must button my cape.

 The wind puffed and yanked the cape. But the man just held the cape close to his chest. At last the wind was puffed out.

 Puff, puff, pant, whish.

123

You are strong, Wind, but look at me. I can make him take off his cape.

 The sun began to smile on the man.

 Smile, smile. Shine, shine.

 The wind has left. I am glad the sun is out. I can unbutton my cape.

 SMILE, SMILE.

 That sun is so hot. I will take off my cape.

 So the man slipped off his cape and the wind lost the contest.

 Remember, Wind, if you wish to be a winner, a smile is better than a bad temper.

	Trickers
didn't	can't
isn't	don't
wasn't	won't

pigeon   book

The Spingle Spangle Talent Show

Chapter 1

The Superkids were putting on a show.
Doc made a list of jobs and acts.

The Spingle Spangle Talent Show

1. Doc   Set up benches.
2. Hot Rod   Fix up the bus.
3. Lily   Sell tickets.
4. Cass   Get stuff for the show.
5. Sal   Sing.
6. Tic, Tac, Toc   Tell jokes.
7. Oswald, Alf, Icky, and Frits   Do an animal act.

Doc taped her list on the bus.

The kids began setting up the show.

But Ettabetta got on the bus.

"Doc didn't put me on the list," Ettabetta said. "She didn't want me in the show."

The Spingle Spangle Talent Show

1. Doc   Set up benches.
2. Hot Rod   Fix up the bus.
3. Lily   Sell tickets.
4. Cass   Get stuff for the show.
5. Sal   Sing.
6. Tic, Tac, Toc   Tell jokes.
7. Oswald, Alf, Icky, and Frits   Do an animal act.

Chapter 2

The show began.

Doc said, "Sal will sing."

Sal got on stilts and sang.

"A fish goes flip, flop.

A duck goes quack, quack,
quack.

A frog goes ribbit, ribbit.

And a bug goes crick,
crick, crack!"

CLAP CLAP CLAP CLAP

"That was fantastic!" said Doc.

"That was rotten," said Ettabetta.

"The Super Chickens are next!"
said Doc.

132

"What a bunch of clucks!" said Ettabetta.

Doc said, "The
next act is
The Octopus Band!"

Oswald sang.
"The Octopus Band
is the best in the land.
Lots of jazz and razzamatazz!"

"Thanks, Octopus Band," said Doc.

"I can't stand it!" said Ettabetta. "The show is ending, and I wasn't in it!"

Doc said, "The best act is last. It is Ettabetta!"

Ettabetta didn't get up.

"Where did Ettabetta go?" asked the Superkids.

"I am sitting on the bus," said Ettabetta.

Doc ran to Ettabetta.

"Will you do an act?" asked Doc.

"No!" said Ettabetta. "You left me off
the list!"

Doc said, "I didn't mean to. I just
forgot to put your name on the list.
You must do an act. The show will flop
if you don't."

"Well, O.K.," said Ettabetta.

Ettabetta ran off the bus.

"I am an acrobat!" she said.
She smiled.

CLAP

CLAP

CLAP

Ettabetta did leg splits.
She did handstands and backbends.

Ettabetta did flips.
Then she did handsprings!

"Thanks, Ettabetta!" said Doc.
"What a fantastic ending for the
Spingle Spangle Talent Show!"

Buster

Chapter 1

Ring-a-ling!

 "Hi!"

 "Hi, Cass. This is Frits. Buster is back!"

 "Buster?"

 "Buster is the pigeon that was in my attic last summer."

 "Oh, I remember. Buster broke his wing. You helped him get better."

 "Buster is making a nest in my attic."

 "Let's go to the bus and tell the rest of the kids!"

Frits said, "I bet you can't tell what I
have in my attic."

"A hippopotamus?" asked Tic.

"A dragon?" asked Toc.

"No," giggled Frits. "Let's go look."

The Superkids ran up to the attic.

"Look!" said Frits. "Buster is back!
Isn't he fantastic?"

"Frits," said Cass. "Buster is not a he."

"What?" asked Frits.

"Buster is a girl," said Cass. "Look in the nest."

"An egg!" said Frits.

"When will the egg hatch?"
asked Hot Rod.

"I have a book about pigeons,"
said Oswald. "It can tell us
when the egg will hatch."

Cass, Oswald, and Frits left to get
the book. The other Superkids went
back to the bus.

Chapter 2

Here is what it said in Oswald's book:

1. A pigeon makes a nest
   out of sticks and twigs.

2. A pigeon has two eggs.

3. It takes 17 days for the eggs
   to hatch.

"Buster has only one egg," said Cass.

The kids went back to check Buster's nest.

"Look," said Oswald. "There are TWO eggs!"

"Don't tell the other kids," said Frits. "Let's just bring them back when the eggs hatch."

"O.K.," said Cass and Oswald. "We won't tell."

Buster was a good sitter. For 17 days, Buster sat on the eggs. On the last day, the Superkids came to visit Buster. The Superkids waited and waited.

"Hatch fast, egg," said Sal. "I am getting a cramp from sitting so long."

Just then, Buster fluttered her wings and got off the nest.

"Oh, look!" said Hot Rod. "There are two eggs!"

Chapter 3

"Buster has twins," whispered Lily.

Two little bills pecked at the eggshells.

"You can do it, little pigeons," said Cass.

The little pigeons kicked and thrashed.
At last, the eggshells split. The little
pigeons tumbled out.

The kids clapped and smiled.

"These pigeons are so little," said Sal.

"What can we name them?" asked Frits.

"What about Hot and Rod?" asked Hot Rod.

"That is not so hot, you wing-ding,"
said Cass.

"That is it!" said Lily. "We can name
the pigeons Wing and Ding."

"I like that," said Frits. "Hi, Wing!
Hi, Ding!"